Usborne Christmas Activity Book

Written by
Rebecca Gilpin, James Maclaine
and Lucy Bowman

Designed and illustrated by
Erica Harrison, Jan McCafferty,
Fred Blunt, Emily Beevers, Non Figg,
Lauren Ellis and Cecilia Johansson

Edited by Fiona Watt

You'll find the answers and solutions
to the puzzles on pages 61-64.

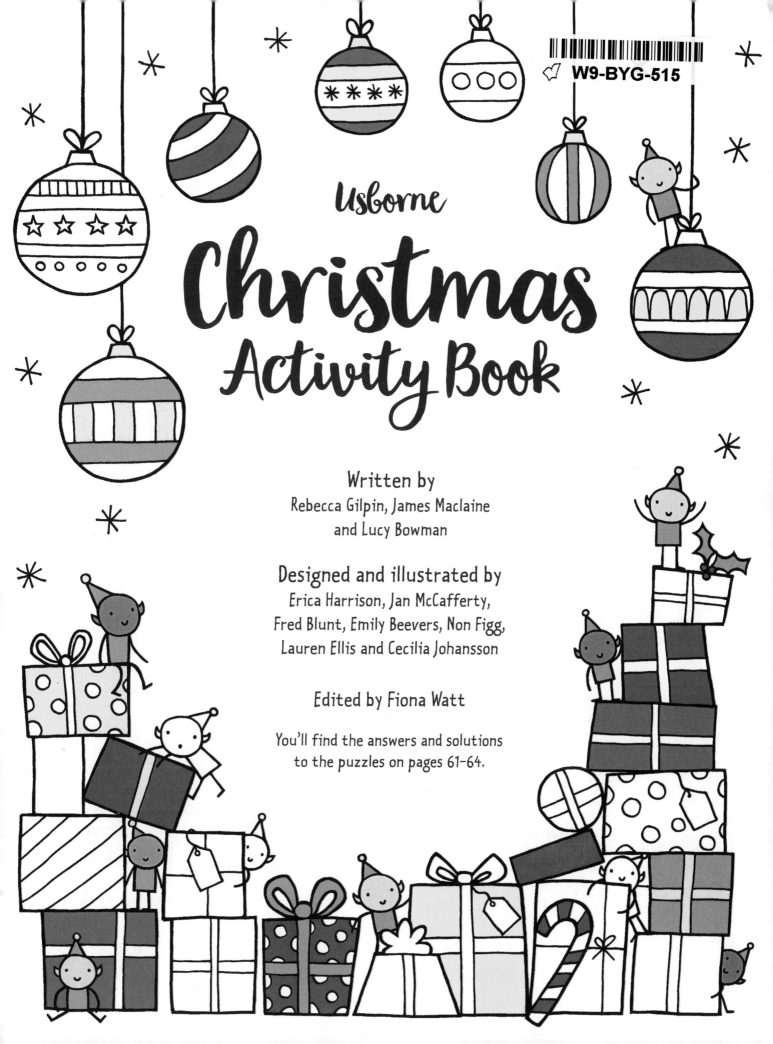

COUNTDOWN TO CHRISTMAS

Fill in the pictures, day by day, in the exciting countdown to Christmas. If it's already Christmas, just fill them all in.

MERRY CHRISTMAS!

SUPER SANTAS

WHICH SANTA?
There are four naughty imposters in this Santa line-up. Can you identify the real Santa from these clues?

☆ He's wearing a belt.
☆ He isn't extremely tall.

☆ He has a neat beard.
☆ He's lost the ball from his hat.

..... is the real Santa.

DOODLE
on these Santas.

Doodle different expressions on their faces.

Draw Santa hats.

This Santa's going somewhere sunny – give him sunglasses.

You could add rosy cheeks.

SANTA'S ART

Fill in the squares to find out what picture Santa's admiring. One square has been added to get you started.

Each of the references below is a square. Cross them off as you fill in the squares.

 G10, I10

D4, I2, K7, B1, M3, F3, E6, K4, B3, F7, J3, M5, D2, K6, C4, N2, D5, I1, K2, E7, K3, F4, B2, L5, D6, M4, D3, J7, N3, E4, K5, B4, I3

F9, I13, J10, C8, L9, G12, I8, G7, K8, D9, H11, M8, J12, F11, G8, H7, I11, G13, H14, J9, E8, H10, F12, L8, G14, I7, J11, D8, H12, G9, H13, J8, I9, F10, H8, E9, I12, K9, F8, I14, G11, H9

H15

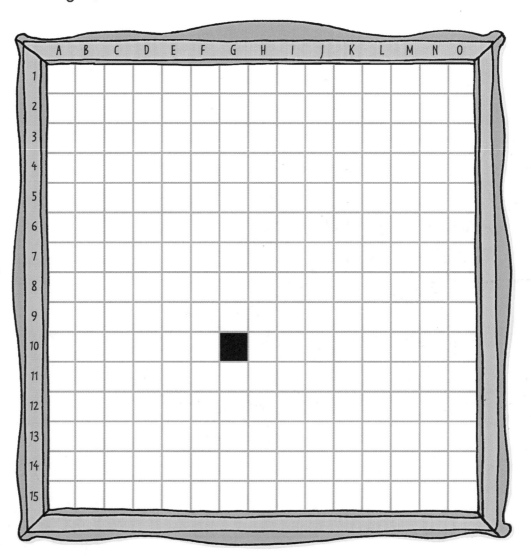

SANTA NEEDS HELP

Santa needs to fill his sack with presents, but the elves have been playing instead of finishing most of the toys.

There are four kinds of toys, but only one of each kind is complete. To help Santa fill his sack, find each finished toy and fill it in. Then, complete the other toys and fill them in, too.

5

TREE DECORATIONS

CHRISTMAS LIGHTS

The white lights below need to be filled in before the string can go on a Christmas tree. Can you do this, making sure to follow the sequence?

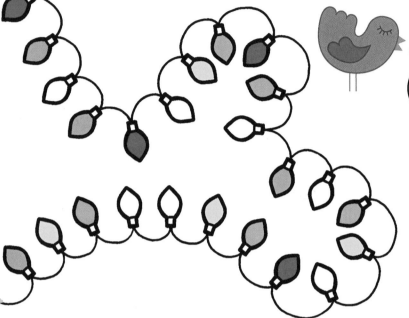

DOODLE
patterns on these decorations.

SPARKLING TREE

Decorate this tree by filling in each shape using a pen that matches the dot inside it.

WORD PAIRS

Each of these decorations has half a Christmas word on it. Complete the words by linking each pair of half words with a line.

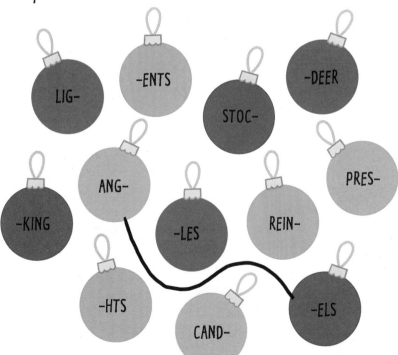

LIG-

-ENTS

-DEER

STOC-

ANG-

PRES-

-KING

-LES

REIN-

-HTS

CAND-

-ELS

FESTIVE FINDS

Spot and fill in the following:

☆ 3 striped decorations
☆ 2 birds

☆ 5 stars
☆ 3 decorations with spots

☆ 4 bells
☆ 2 hearts

Then, fill in the rest of the decorations, too.

7

SANTA'S WORKSHOP

The elves are busy in the workshop. Can you spot and circle everything on the list?

☆ four mice
☆ five toy soldiers
☆ seven candy canes
☆ four red scarves
☆ a silver belt buckle
☆ a hat missing its bell
☆ a striped stocking
☆ eight building blocks
☆ two tennis balls

HEADING HOME

Everyone's rushing to get home for Christmas. Race through these puzzles and see if you can crack them.

ON THE ROAD

The roads are crammed with cars as people take their Christmas trees and presents home. Can you spot and fill in the following in this picture?

☆ eight Christmas trees ☆ twenty presents ☆ a broken-down car ☆ a car with four people inside
☆ four dogs ☆ a reindeer ☆ two turkeys ☆ Santa in a sports car

RACING HOME

Dad needs to use the quickest route to get home for Christmas. Whichever way he goes, there are lots of obstacles, each with a different number of points. The lower the number of points, the quicker the journey. Which way should he go?

Hole in the road = 1

Red light = 2

Traffic jam = 3

Roadworks = 4

Do any calculations here:

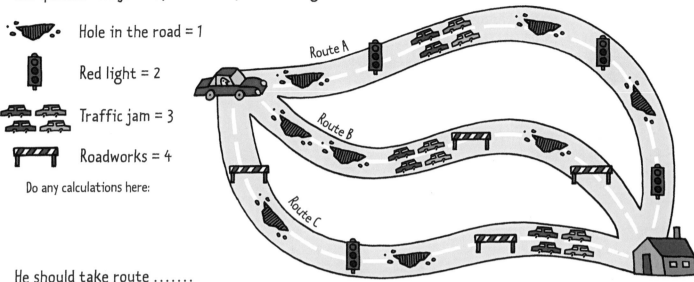

He should take route ....

HOW LONG?

How many minutes will it take each person to get home? The clocks show what time they're leaving and what time they'll arrive.

A

.... minutes

B

4:20   4:40

.... minutes

C

.... minutes

WHICH WAY HOME?

The girl in square B4 has finished shopping and wants to go home. To find out her route and see where she lives, cross off these squares: C2, G3, B1, D4, G1, A3, C1, E2, G4, C5, F1, D5, A1, E4, G2, E1, B5, F2, G5, A4, D1, C4, D2, A2, B2. One square has already been crossed off, to get you started.

Draw a line through the squares with no Xs to see the girl's route. The final square is where her house is.

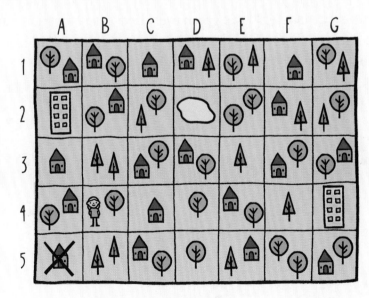

Her house is in square ....

11

ICE MONSTERS

RUN AWAY!

Draw a line as quickly as you can through this frozen labyrinth, away from the monster. Don't bump into any of the walls with your pen.

HO HO HO!

Q. What do you get if you cross the Abominable Snowman with a kangaroo?

A. A giant fur coat with one front pocket.

EYEBALL BLIZZARD

One-eyed monsters have green eyes, two-eyed monsters have red eyes, and three-eyed monsters have blue eyes. How many monsters are lost in this blizzard?

Answer . . . .

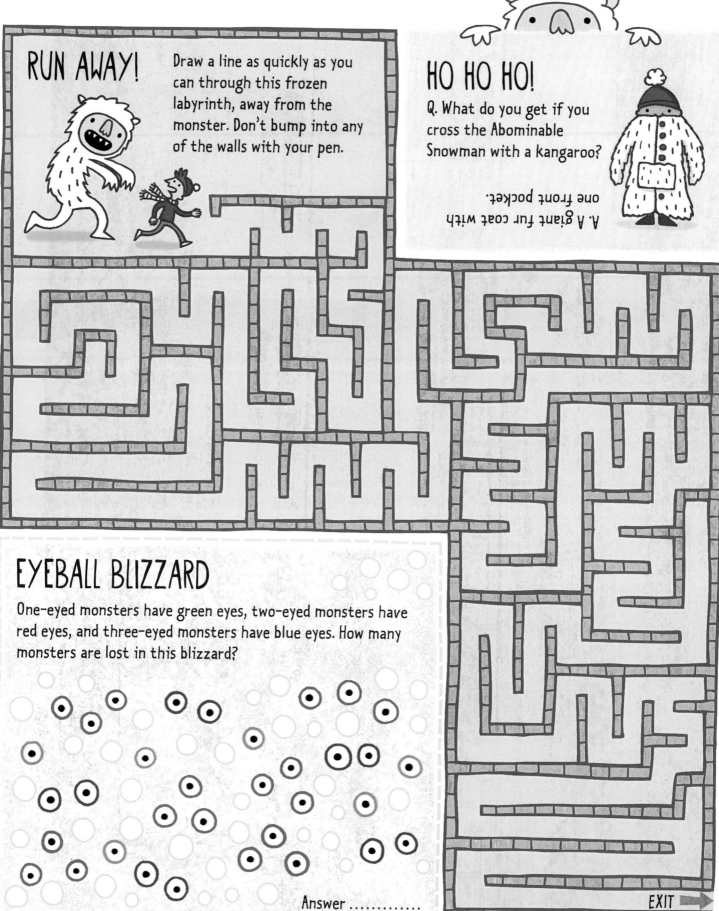

EXIT ▶

ICY BITES

Bitter Boris will only eat the coldest foods. Can you unscramble the letters in the words to see what's on his plate?

And what's in his glass?

CIDE ATE

DOLC IPAZZ

EIC MARCE

OBTRES

ZOFERN APES

SNOWED OUT

Can you link these monsters with their identical twins who got caught in a snowstorm?

WHAT'S DIFFERENT?

Each of these snowflake monsters is slightly different. Circle the different details in each one.

13

SNOWY VILLAGE

Lots of elves live in this snowy village, nestling beneath the mountains. Doodle more houses, elves, trees and reindeer, then fill in the rest of the picture.

DRAW AN ELF

1. Draw an elf's head and body.

2. Add a face, arms and legs.

3. Add ears, then draw a pointed hat.

CHRISTMAS ON THE SLOPES

SKIING RACE

There are four people in this race, and the winner is the one with the most points. Add up the numbers on each skier's route, and take off points for each swerve or fall. Write in each skier's total, then draw around the winner.

(!) Swerve = -1

/!\ Fall = -2

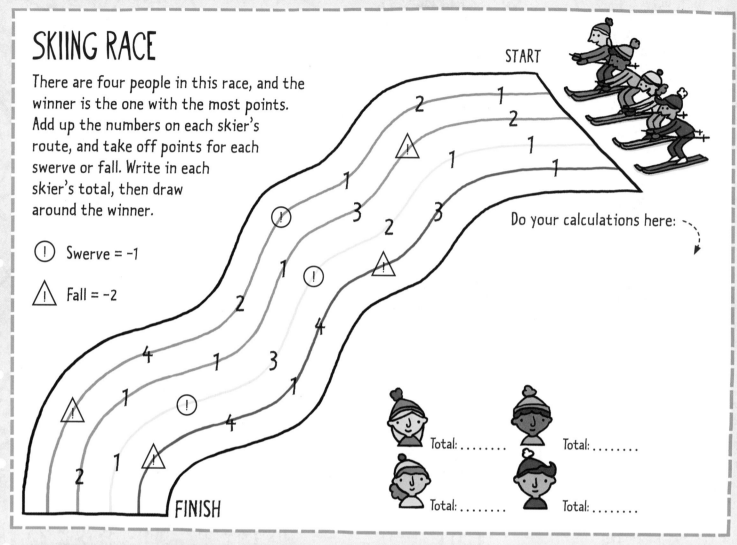

START

Do your calculations here: →

Total: . . . .
Total: . . . .
Total: . . . .
Total: . . . .

FINISH

DAREDEVIL SNOWBOARDERS Fill in these snowboarders.

SKI LIFT CONUNDRUM

Seven adults and five children want to travel to the top of this ski lift. Looking at the picture and clues, are there enough pods to take them all there?

YES/NO

CLUES:
☆ A blue pod can carry one adult.
☆ A red pod can carry one adult and one child.
☆ A green pod can carry two adults and one child.
☆ A yellow pod can carry three children.
☆ A purple pod can carry two adults.
☆ An orange pod has to remain empty.

SPEEDY TOBOGGAN

Draw a line as fast as you can, to take this toboggan to the bottom of the track.
Don't crash into the sides!

WINTER ACTIVITIES

There are lots of fun winter activities, and several are listed below, but what are they? Once you've unscrambled the words, link each activity to the correct picture with a line.

 A

 B

 C

1 GINSKI

D

2 SIGNNOBRADOW

3 NINGOTBOGGA

4 BALWOLNS THFIG

E

5 ECI GATKINS

17

FESTIVE FILL-IN

Grab some pens or pencils and fill
in the Christmassy shapes...

SANTA'S HOUSE

Santa has just got out of bed, and there's lots to do. He needs to pick up all the things on his list in the order they appear, then feed his reindeer. Can you find the shortest route for him? Draw a line for Santa's route, and cross things off the list as you get to them.

Can you find six sneaky elves?

SANTA'S LIST:

Santa's hat
A purple umbrella
Santa's belt
Santa's coat
Santa's sack
A teddy bear
A blue striped present
Santa's boots
Hot chocolate and cookies
Carrots for the reindeer
Feed the reindeer

See if you can spot
three little birds.

AROUND THE WORLD

People in different countries celebrate Christmas with their own traditions and stories. Their celebrations may take place in the weeks before and after Christmas:

 In Sweden, the Christmas season begins with the festival of St. Lucia on 13th December. The eldest girl in each house wears white robes and a crown of lights on her head.

 In the build-up to Christmas, markets are set up in Germany selling food, hot drinks, decorations, candles and toys. They are called Weihnachtsmärkte.

 According to Greek legend, mischievous creatures called Kallikantzaroi come out at Christmas time to play pranks. People keep fires lit in the hope that they will keep the creatures away.

 In Italian folklore, La Befana is an old woman who flies on a broomstick. If children have been good, she puts presents in their stockings, but if they have been bad, she leaves them coal.

URN OF FATE

In Italy, children take turns pulling wrapped boxes from the 'Urn of Fate'. Some of the boxes contain presents, and some are empty. Draw a circle around the person who gets an empty box this time.

CHRISTMAS FOOD

People all over the world celebrate Christmas by eating different foods. See how many of these foods you can find in the letters below. The names may be written across, up, down, backwards and even diagonally.

```
S N G K R I N G L E H
H M D S N A W F V G R
R U A H L A C A B V O
P E P P A R K A K O R
I L K F V Y M L R P F
A S J T E U C X C R M
K F I K D A O P J A B
W E R L K F H M I C L
U U S T O L L E N D X
T L P E Z V F T E R I
```

KRINGLE
A Danish bread in the shape of a knot.

TURKEY
In England, turkeys are roasted and served with stuffing.

STOLLEN
A German bread loaf filled with dried fruit, nuts and spices.

BACALHAU
Salted cod, served with potatoes. Popular in Portugal.

PEPPARKAKOR
Thin, crisp ginger snaps from Sweden.

CARP
A large fish served with stewed cabbage, often eaten in Poland.

Many of these foods are enjoyed in several countries at Christmas.

MERRY CHRISTMAS

There are lots of different ways to say "Merry Christmas". Here are some for you to try saying.

FINLAND – HYVÄÄ JOULUA
(say 'hoo-vah-yo-loo-ah')

FRANCE – JOYEUX NOËL
(say 'joy-yuh-no-well')

SPAIN – FELIZ NAVIDAD
(say 'fell-eeth-nah-vee-dad')

INDONESIA – SELAMAT NATAL
(say 'seh-la-mat-na-tal')

WALES – NADOLIG LLAWEN
(say 'nad-or-lig-hlah-wen')

DID YOU KNOW?

On Bondi Beach in Australia, people wear Santa hats on Christmas Day, even though it's hot and sunny.

WINTRY TREES

TREE MAZE

This boy has wandered away from his friends in the forest.
Follow the outline of the trees to help him find his way to them.

Fill in all the birds and squirrels you can find.

START

FINISH

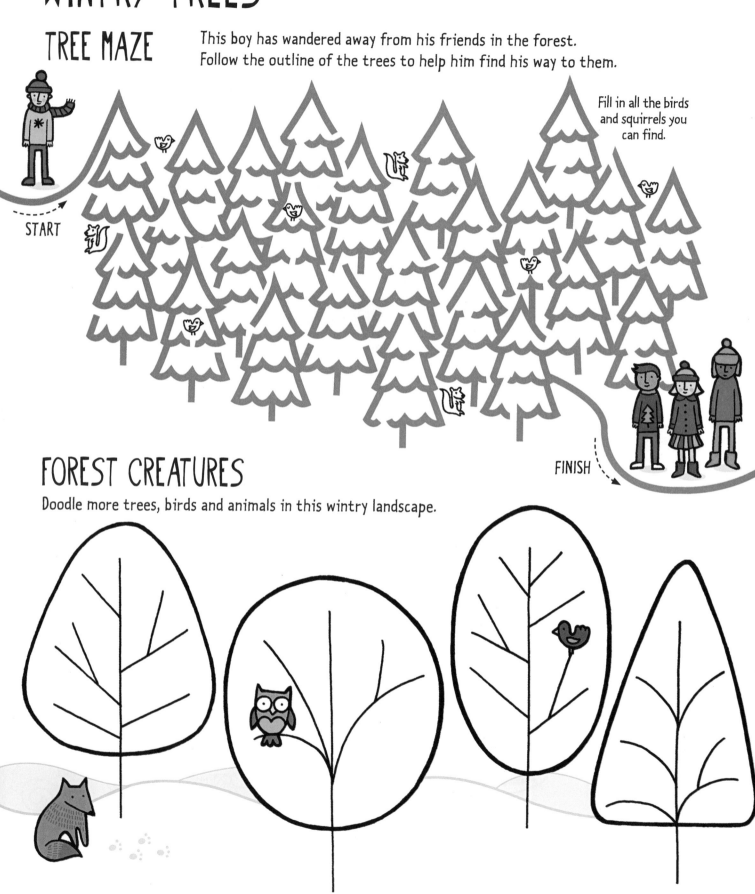

FOREST CREATURES

Doodle more trees, birds and animals in this wintry landscape.

CHOOSING A TREE

The children below have come to choose a perfect Christmas tree, but they all want different things. Which tree will they take home?

NUTCRACKER CHRISTMAS

The Nutcracker is a very popular Christmas ballet. Complete the puzzles as you follow its story.

On Christmas Eve, Clara receives a Nutcracker doll from her godfather,
but her mean brother grabs the doll and breaks it...

PIECING TOGETHER

Can you help Clara's godfather fix the broken Nutcracker?
Link the correct parts together with a line.

The completed Nutcracker should look like this.

That night, Clara can't sleep, so she creeps downstairs to check on the Nutcracker. As midnight strikes, Clara starts to shrink until she's no bigger than a mouse. Suddenly, an army of mice attack her, but at this perilous moment, the Nutcracker miraculously comes to life...

CROWN THE KING

The mice all have identical twins, except for their leader, the Mouse King. Find the pairs, then draw a crown on the Mouse King's head.

Together, Clara and the Nutcracker defeat the Mouse King. The Nutcracker turns into a handsome prince, and he and Clara fly off on a magical journey...

Their journey takes them to the Land of Sweets, where they see ice-cream mountains and marshmallow flowers...

DOODLE windows and doors on the marzipan houses...

Fill everything in, too.

...and add patterns and faces on the lollipop trees.

The pair tell their tale to the Sugar Plum Fairy, who rewards them with a party of dancing and feasting...

Six things below wouldn't please my sweet tooth. Cross them out!

THE SUGAR PLUM FAIRY'S FEAST

Full of food and overwhelmed by all she's seen, Clara drifts off to sleep. When she wakes up, she's back home, beside the Christmas tree, with the Nutcracker doll in her arms.

PLAYFUL PENGUINS

ICE RACE

Three penguins are sliding on their bellies, racing towards the finish line. There are things in their way that will add time or speed up their route. Which penguin wins the race?

 Hungry leopard seal to avoid = add 5 seconds

Very slippery ice = knock off 2 seconds

Penguin egg to collect = add 3 seconds

START

 FINISH

A

B

C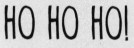

ANSWER:

....

HO HO HO!

Q. What's black and white, and goes up and down?

A. A penguin on a trampoline!

PENGUIN HIDE AND SEEK

There are six baby penguins hidden in this group of Emperor penguins. Can you spot and circle them all?

28

DRAW A PENGUIN

Draw a head
and body.

Add two wings.

Add eyes...

...and a beak.

Fill it in.

Try drawing
one sideways,
too.

Fill the snow
with penguins
having fun.

PENGUIN PAIRS

All but one of these penguins
match a silhouette. Draw lines
between the pairs, then circle the
one that's left.

PENGUIN SPOTTING

There are many different kinds of penguin. How many names
can you find on the penguin's tummy?

The names of
penguins can go
up, down, across,
diagonally, or even
backwards.

EMPEROR

FAIRY

GALAPAGOS

GENTOO

HUMBOLDT

KING

MACARONI

ROCKHOPPER

```
G E N T O O F C S T
A M F A D Y G N I K
L H A K I G R Y D T R
A R M C S H E I T A C
P O A I A K O J A B
A R Q R Y R Z S U F
G E H U M B O L D T
O P I T O C L N X J
S M D S G M E F I Z
R E P P O H K C O R
```

29

WELCOME, SANTA!

NOTE TO SANTA

Some of the words in this note are mixed up, so Santa may not know what he needs to deliver. Can you figure out the words, so that Santa can read the note and deliver the presents?

READ ....

OSUEH ....

DREENEIR ....

IRDET ....

KATESDROAB ....

SKOBO ....

DOOG ....

It's Christmas Eve, and Santa's on his way...

> READ Santa
>
> Welcome to our OSUEH. We hope that you and the DREENEIR are well and not too IRDET. Please may we have a KATESDROAB and some SKOBO? We've tried so hard to be DOOG this year!
>
> Thank you, Santa!
>
> Love from
> Emily and Luke XX

BEDTIME

These children are rushing to be in bed before Santa arrives. Count the footprints to find out how many steps each child has to take to get into bed. The one with the fewest steps will be in bed first. Who will be first?

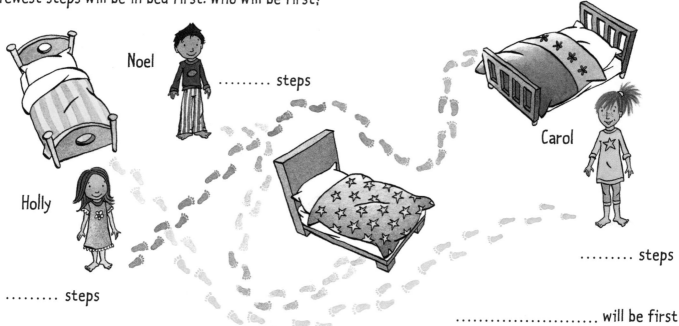

Noel .... steps

Carol

Holly

.... steps

.... steps

.... will be first

STOCKINGS
Santa's crammed lots of presents into these stockings. Add patterns to make them look really Christmassy.

LATE AT NIGHT

Late on Christmas Eve, Magnus the dog is dozing by the fire. Then, something happens. Look at these two pictures – what has changed, and what do you think might have happened?

TWINKLING LIGHTS

At Christmas, people decorate their homes with sparkling lights and candles.

TANGLED LIGHTS

Find the route that will lead this mouse to his friend. He can't walk over any of the lights.

SPARKLING STAR LIGHTS

How many star lights are there here? Fill them in as you count them.

There are . . . . stars.

BRIGHT BULB SUDOKU

Fill in these light bulbs so that there's one red, one blue, one green and one yellow bulb in each row, column and 4-square box.

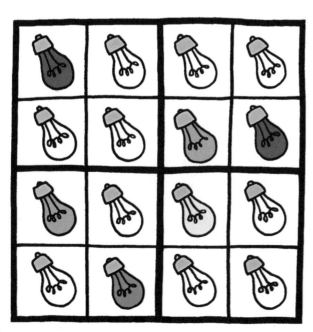

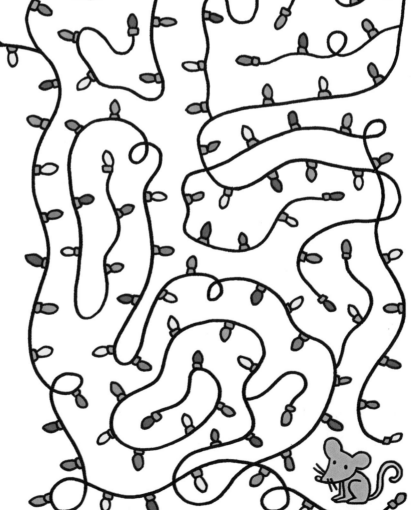

LIGHT THE LIGHTS

Each of these sets of lights follows a different sequence.
Figure out each sequence, then fill in the lights that aren't lit.

CANDLE CONUNDRUM

Starting at candle A, and following the direction of the arrows, which route to candle B takes you through the most candles? Once you know, draw the route.

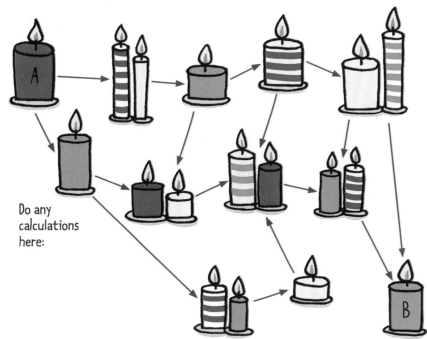

Do any calculations here:

ILLUMINATING WORDS

In this space, write as many words as you can to describe Christmas lights:

DAZZLING

SHIMMERING

FESTIVE FELINES

Finish these Christmassy cats, using pens and pencils.

Give this cat a Santa hat.

Maybe add some presents?

Doodle lights and decorations, too.

HO HO HO HOUNDS

Get these dogs ready for the festive season by giving them costumes and presents.

Some dogs could wear reindeer antlers...

...or a Christmas sweater...

....or maybe an angel's halo.

This dog wants a bone.

REINDEER IN TRAINING

ROUTE PLANNER

Can you help this reindeer find the route that will take him, the other reindeer and Santa around the world on Christmas Eve? They have to pass through every star, but they can't take the same flight path more than once.

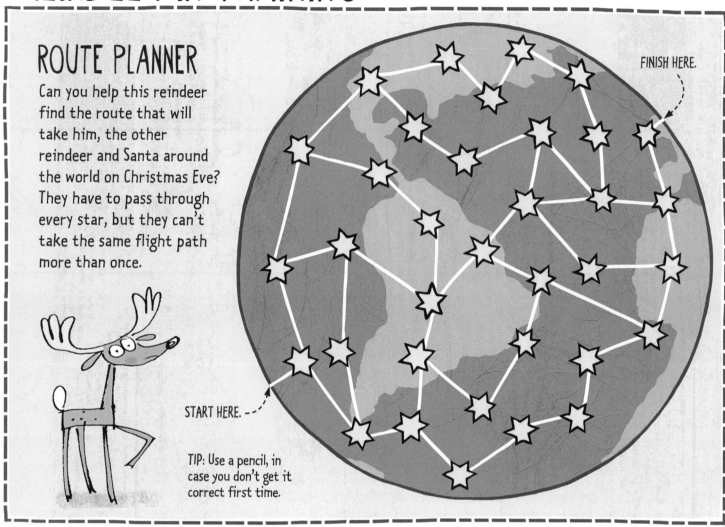

FINISH HERE.

START HERE.

TIP: Use a pencil, in case you don't get it correct first time.

DOWNTIME

The reindeer are resting before their big flight. But which reindeer is in each stable? Read the clues below, then write the correct names on the doors.

☆ Cupid is next to Rudolph.
☆ Prancer is in a stable at one of the ends.
☆ Dasher is between Vixen and Comet.
☆ Blitzen has the biggest antlers.
☆ Dancer is farthest away from Rudolph.
☆ Comet has big eyes.
☆ Donner is next to Dancer.
☆ Vixen has no antlers.

Rudolph

RACING REINDEER

Which reindeer comes first, second and third in this race?

TIP: Look at the information on the sign.

Reindeer C runs along three sections of track in the same time that Reindeer B runs along two sections and Reindeer A runs along one section.

1ST ....
2ND ....
3RD ....

DID YOU KNOW?
Reindeer have hairy noses that help keep them warm while grazing in the snow.

START

FINISH

FESTIVE PUZZLES

See if you can solve these fun puzzles as you celebrate Christmas.

CANDY CANES

Fill in the striped canes with a red pen and the others with a green pen. Are there more red or green canes?

There are more .... canes.

PRESENT SPOTTING

Can you find these three presents in the picture below?

1   2   3

CHRISTMASSY FIREPLACE

The white mouse needs to get back to his mouse hole, through the fireplace maze. Which way should he go?

See how many words you can make from the phrase

CHRISTMAS DECORATIONS

Each time, only use each letter the number of times it appears.

Write your words in this space.

SNOWSTORM SHAPE

A shape is hidden in this snowstorm, but what is it? Join the even numbers with lines, starting with the smallest and going up to the biggest.

The shape is a ....

15   35   16   9   23
1
        29   43   11
    27
20   18   14   49   12
        33
    22   37
    2   5   10
51   3
    21   6   17
7   19   41
    4   39   8
47   13   25   45
            31

STARS SUDOKU

Fill in the stars, so that each row, column and 4-square box has one orange, one red, one yellow and one blue star in it.

DING DONG!

Which string does this elf need to pull to ring the biggest bell? Circle the correct answer.

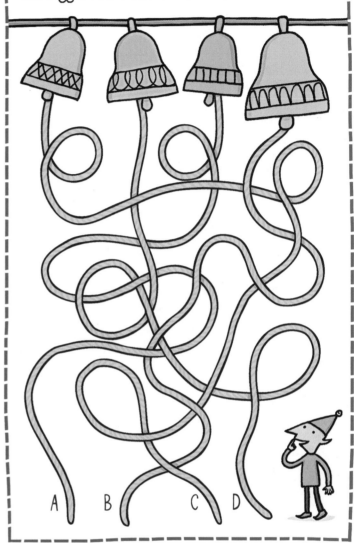

A   B   C   D

TREE TROUBLE

These Christmas trees have fallen over and landed in a heap. How many are there? Draw over the outlines as you count them.

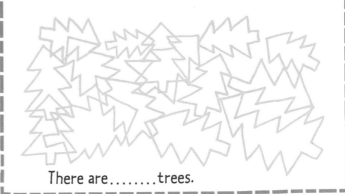

There are........trees.

WINTER WONDERLAND

Use pens or pencils to brighten up
this winter wonderland.

RED AND GREEN
DRESS THE ELVES

Some elves wear red and others wear green. Follow the instructions to find out how many elves you should fill in red. Then, fill the rest in green.

Cross out:

☆ the number of legs three reindeer have
☆ the four smallest numbers
☆ how many eyes seven elves have
☆ the six biggest numbers
☆ the number of letters in 'Christmas'

25   7
8   5   19   22
12   14   16   9
21   4   15   17

ODDS AND EVENS

Draw over the shapes with an even number of sides in red and those with an odd number of sides in green. Are there more 'even' or 'odd' shapes?

There are more .... shapes.

TREE-ANGLES

Can you find and circle these three patterned triangles on the tree below?

CANDIED CODES

Match the puzzles A, B and C with codes 1, 2 and 3, then find the Christmassy word hidden in each one.

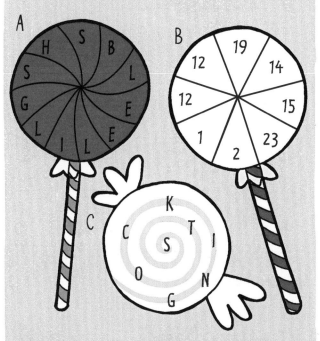

1 Starting in the middle, the letters are written in a spiral.

Puzzle:........

Word: ....

2 Each number represents a letter in the alphabet: 1 is A, 2 is B, 3 is C, 4 is D... Starting at '12 o'clock', the word is written in a circle going clockwise.

Puzzle:........

Word: ....

3 Starting at the top and going around and around clockwise, every other letter spells out the word.

Puzzle:........

Word: ....

Write the alphabet here: --->

HO HO HO!

Q. What's small and green, and red in the face?

A. An embarrassed elf.

DID YOU KNOW?

In some countries, people give poinsettia plants at Christmas. The red parts of the plant are often mistaken for flowers, but they're actually leaves.

TOY SHOPPING

This bustling toy department is crammed with people shopping for Christmas. Can you spot the following?

- ☆ a panda
- ☆ someone holding a rabbit
- ☆ two purple dinosaurs
- ☆ a guitar
- ☆ a spaceman
- ☆ a reindeer decoration
- ☆ a boy with blue shoes
- ☆ three cowboys
- ☆ a girl with a jigsaw puzzle

CHRISTMAS MYSTERIES

Can you solve the puzzles on these pages?

CRYPTIC INVITATION

Ben's given you a mysterious invitation to his Christmas party. Using the map and the instructions below, can you find your way there?

You're invited to my party, but where is it taking place? See if you can find it! Hope you make it... Ben

☆ Walk East.
☆ Take the second road on the left.
☆ Walk North.
☆ Enter the park.
☆ Walk along the path.
☆ Take the first left.
☆ Leave the park.
☆ Go West.
☆ Take the path going North.
☆ Turn left.
☆ The party is in the second house on the left.

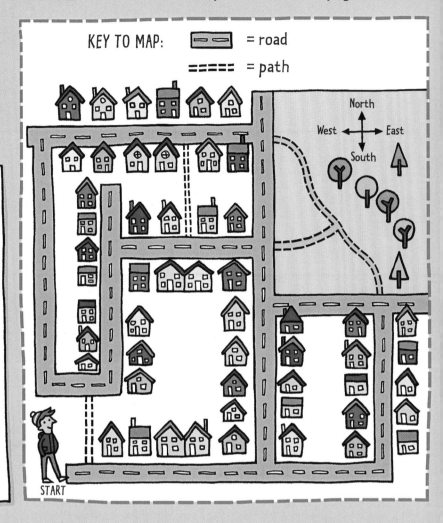

FESTIVE LETTERS

Kian's been sent some Christmas letters, and he's trying to guess who they're from before opening them. Draw a line from each envelope to the person who sent it. Has anyone's letter got lost and failed to arrive?

I love stars!

My letter got wet in the rain.

I write in CAPITAL LETTERS.

I have very big handwriting.

I have a cat that walks on everything!

Serena

Casper

Stella

Joe

Natalia

PRESENT RENDEZVOUS

Beth wants to meet Billy to give him a present, so she's sent him a secret message on this piece of newspaper. What is Beth's message to Billy?

CHRISTMAS MYSTERY

Until Monday, the Santa at the local department store was bringing smiles to the faces of all the children with his kindness and loud jolly laugh. But he has not been seen for two days, leaving only questions, and a Christmas mystery.

Today is Christmas Eve, which may be a clue: perhaps our Santa had to go because he had lots of other things to do before Christmas..?

....

....

....

CHRISTMAS MOVIE MIX-UP

These shots are all from a movie, but they're in the wrong order. Which order should they be in? Write numbers 1–4 in the stars.

CHRISTMAS BONE BRAIN-TEASER

Noodle the dog is really excited because he's been given a bone, but which one is his? Follow the instructions below to find out, then draw a bow on Noodle's bone.

Cross out:
☆ the number of paws Noodle has
☆ the number of minutes in half an hour
☆ the number of days in one week
☆ the answer to eight multiplied by two
☆ the number of bones in this picture
☆ numbers that can be divided by five
☆ the number of eyes Noodle has
☆ four plus four

AT THE MARKET

Enjoy all the toys and tasty treats for sale at a Christmas market.

Can you spot all the things on this list?

☆ two bears
☆ one train
☆ three striped balls
☆ one reindeer toy
☆ five candy canes
☆ one big chocolate heart
☆ two robots
☆ ten marbles

TOY TIME

These handmade toys are for sale, but there's one that doesn't match in each row. Draw a circle around each one.

WOODEN PUZZLE

This stall sells puzzles carved from wood. Which two of these pieces will complete this star?

A   B   C

CHRISTMAS FOOD

There are lots of different snacks and drinks on this stall, but their names are all mixed up. Can you rearrange the letters to see what's for sale?

OTH AHCEOLTCO ....
GSAASUSE   ....
TSEUSCTHN   ....
EGNARDGIEBR   ....
ABDEK TOPOTA ....

DECORATION SUDOKU

This stall sells Christmas tree decorations. Finish the patterns so that there is one of each kind in each row, each column, and each 4-square box.

These are the four different patterns:

DOODLE VILLAGE

Use red and green pens to complete this festive scene.

Doodle more snowflakes in the sky.

Add windows, doors and roofs to the houses.

Fill the bare trees with branches and leaves.

Draw trees in the gaps.

Decorate the snowmen.

Give every mouse you spot a tail.

STARRY NIGHT

A clear winter's night is perfect for star-gazing. Look out for some of the constellations on these pages in the night sky. Complete the starry puzzles, too.

STAR PATH

Can you find a way through this star maze to its middle?

CASSIOPEIA
This constellation can only be seen in the Northern Hemisphere.

GEMINI

Gemini means 'twins' in Latin.

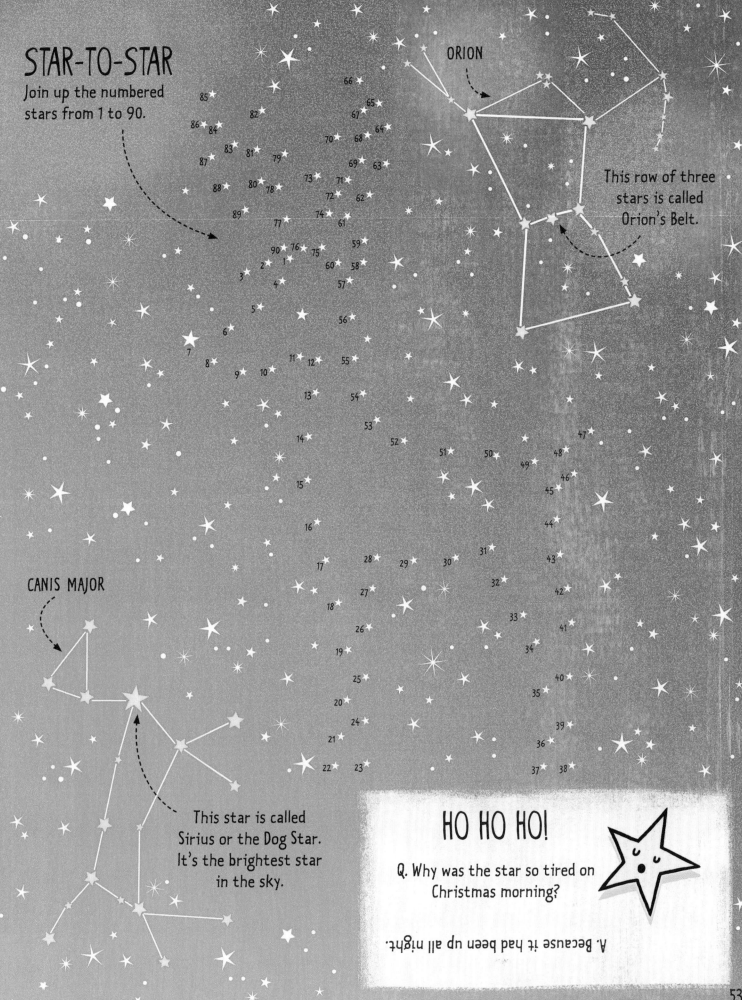

STAR-TO-STAR

Join up the numbered stars from 1 to 90.

ORION

This row of three stars is called Orion's Belt.

CANIS MAJOR

This star is called Sirius or the Dog Star. It's the brightest star in the sky.

HO HO HO!

Q. Why was the star so tired on Christmas morning?

A. Because it had been up all night.

STREET LIGHTS

LIGHT SHAPES
These Christmas light shapes follow a sequence. What is the missing shape?

Fill in the correct shape.

JUMBLE BELLS
Find the two Christmassy words hidden on these bells. Fill in each of the two sets of bells with a different pen.

DE   GA   CO   RA   TI   RLA   NDS   ONS

STAR LIGHTS
Circle the missing detail on one of these lights.

Fill in the Christmas shoppers.

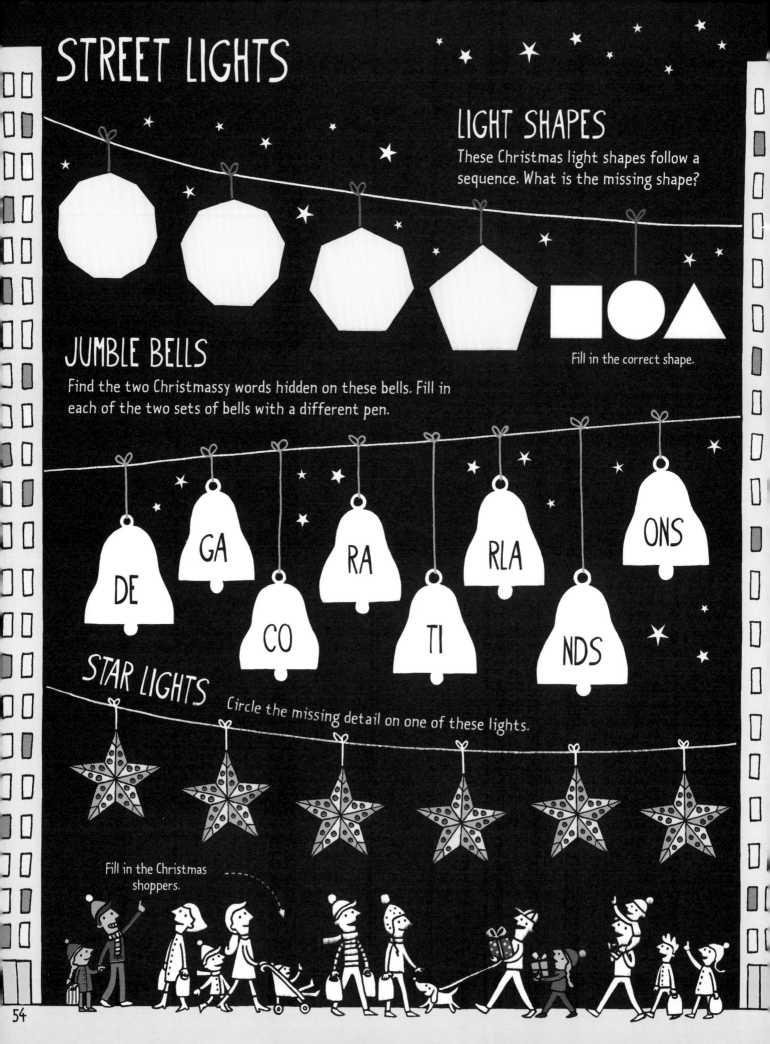

SYMMETRICAL CIRCLES

The patterned light below is symmetrical. When you divide it in half with a straight line, each half is an exact reflection of the other.

Which of the other lights are symmetrical?

BRIGHT BIRDS

Fill in the bird-shaped lights according to the rules below.

☆ Green is between red and orange.
☆ Blue is farthest to the right.
☆ Yellow is next to blue.
☆ Red is farthest away from blue.

DOODLE
patterns on these lights.

SANTA'S ELVES
SORTING LETTERS
Santa gets lots of letters and the elves are busy sorting them.
Draw a line to link each of their letters to the correct pile.

Olaf   Erica   Stefan   Greta   Henrik

| WHITE | NO STAMP | RED | SQUARE | GREEN |

TOYMAKERS

These elves have been making toys, but who has made the most?

A   I made bears.   ..... bears

B   I made cars.   ..... cars

C   I made kites.   ..... kites

HO HO HO!

Q. What's noisier than a giggling elf?

A. Five giggling elves!

56

ELF AND SEEK

The elves should be back at work, but they're hiding instead. How many can you spot? Fill them in as you find them.

I spotted......... elves.

SHIP TOY AHOY!

Santa has asked the elves to make five toy ships. They need to complete the unfinished ones below and draw one more. Can you help?

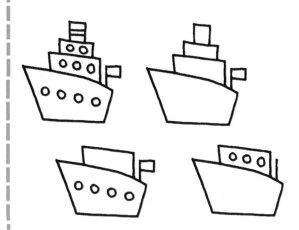

IMPISH IMPOSTER

To keep Santa's workshop secret, each elf has an ID (identity) card. The elves guarding the door have noticed that this 'elf' doesn't match the picture on his card. Can you spot five things that don't match?

Elf ID 25122011

SHOPPING DASH

Everyone's hurrying to do their last-minute Christmas shopping – can you help them by solving these puzzles?

CHRISTMAS CODE

Ted has a list of things to buy, but it's in code, which is slowing him down. Help him by decoding his list, then see if he's picked up the correct things.

TIP: Cross out all the numbers, then cross off every second letter. For example:

T4TE2ED3D

↓

T̷4̷T̷E̷2̷E̷D̷3̷D̷

↓

TED

A7AP2PP1PL9LE4ES3S

....

T8TR1RE5EE7E

....

S2SC9CA1AR4RF3F

....

L6LI3IG1GH9HT4TS8S

....

B2BA5AL9LL6L

....

These are the items that Ted has picked up. Does he have everything that's on his list?

YES / NO

TOY-SHOPPING SPRINT

Max is rushing to buy presents, and he needs to pick up a skateboard, then a doll, pay for them both, then find his way out. He shouldn't pick up any other toys, go over any paths twice or retrace his steps. Which way should he go?

RACE TO PAY

These children are racing to pay for their shopping. To find out who gets to the cash desk first, do all the calculations – whoever has the highest total wins.

Emily
Erica
Eddie

12 – 6 =
2 x 10 =
1 + 2 =

5 x 2 =
8 + 4 =
12 – 7 =

3 + 4 =
10 – 7 =
2 x 8 =

PAY HERE

Do any calculations here:

.............wins, with.......points.

WHICH BAG?

This lady has finished shopping and wants to go home, but which is her bag? Cross off the following to find out:

☆ all the blue bags
☆ every rectangular bag
☆ bags with stripes on them
☆ any bag with red on it

Her bag is number ....

PRESENT PAIRS

Holly needs to buy two of everything for Christmas, but she's in a rush. Link each pair of objects with a line. Has she managed to grab two of each thing?

YES / NO

ANSWERS AND SOLUTIONS

4-5 SUPER SANTAS

WHICH SANTA?:
D is the real Santa.

SANTA NEEDS HELP:

SANTA'S ART:
The picture is of Santa's reindeer, Rudolph.

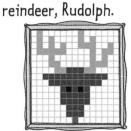

6-7 TREE DECORATIONS

CHRISTMAS LIGHTS:

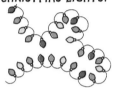

WORD PAIRS:
LIGHTS, STOCKING, ANGELS, PRESENTS, REINDEER, CANDLES

8-9 SANTA'S WORKSHOP

○ mice
○ toy soldiers
○ candy canes
○ red scarves
○ silver belt buckle
○ hat missing its bell
○ striped stocking
○ building blocks
○ tennis balls

10-11 HEADING HOME
ON THE ROAD:

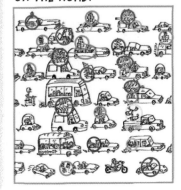

○ Christmas trees
○ dogs
○ presents
○ reindeer
○ broken-down car
○ turkeys
○ car with four people
○ Santa in a sports car

RACING HOME:
Route A = 12, Route B = 14, Route C = 15.
Route A is the quickest one for Dad to take.

HOW LONG?:
A takes 25 minutes.
B takes 20 minutes.
C takes 55 minutes.

WHICH WAY HOME?:
The girl's house is in square E5.
This is her route:

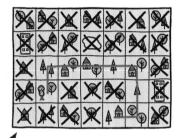

12-13 ICE MONSTERS

EYEBALL BLIZZARD:
There are 17 monsters in the blizzard.

WHAT'S DIFFERENT?:

ICY BITES:
ZOFERN APES = FROZEN PEAS
OBTRES = SORBET
EIC MARCE = ICE CREAM
DOLC IPAZZ = COLD PIZZA
CIDE ATE = ICED TEA

SNOWED OUT:

16-17 CHRISTMAS ON THE SLOPES

SKIING RACE:
Pink = 7, green = 8, yellow = 6, red = 9. Red wins.

SKI LIFT CONUNDRUM:
No. One adult will be left behind.

WINTER ACTIVITIES:
A = 2 SIGNNOBRADOW = snowboarding
B = 3 NINGOTBOGGA = tobogganing
C = 4 BALWOLNS THFIG = snowball fight
D = 1 GINSKI = skiing
E = 5 ECI GATKINS = ice skating

20-21 SANTA'S HOUSE

○ elves
○ birds

Santa's route:

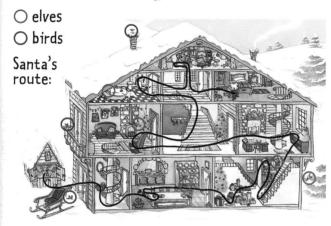

22-23 AROUND THE WORLD

URN OF FATE:

CHRISTMAS FOOD:

24-25 WINTRY TREES

TREE MAZE:

CHOOSING A TREE:

26-27 NUTCRACKER CHRISTMAS

PIECING TOGETHER:

CROWN THE KING:

THE SUGAR PLUM FAIRY'S FEAST:

28-29 PLAYFUL PENGUINS

ICE RACE: Penguin A wins the race.

PENGUIN HIDE AND SEEK:

PENGUIN PAIRS:

PENGUIN SPOTTING:

30-31 WELCOME, SANTA!

NOTE TO SANTA:
READ = dear, OSUEH = house, DREENEIR = reindeer,
IRDET = tired, KATESDROAB = skateboard,
SKOBO = books, DOOG = good

BEDTIME:
Noel takes 22 steps, Holly takes 30, and
Carol takes 28. Noel will be in bed first.

LATE AT NIGHT:
The time on the clock has changed,
Magnus the dog has woken up, the
fire and candles have all gone out, the
cushion on the chair is now squashed,
some milk has been drunk, a cookie has
been eaten, the floor is covered in soot
and dirty footprints, and Christmas
presents have appeared... Santa was here!

32–33 TWINKLING LIGHTS

TANGLED LIGHTS:

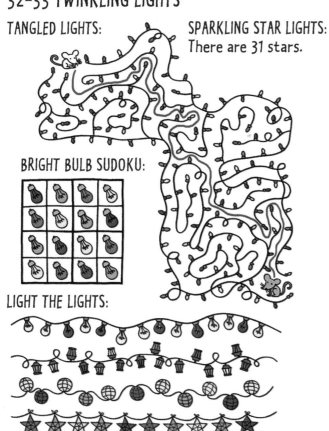

SPARKLING STAR LIGHTS:
There are 31 stars.

BRIGHT BULB SUDOKU:

LIGHT THE LIGHTS:

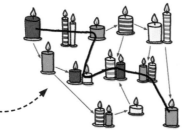

CANDLE CONUNDRUM:
This route takes you through the most candles: 11.

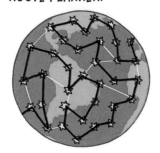

36–37 REINDEER IN TRAINING

ROUTE PLANNER:

DOWNTIME:
From left to right: Prancer, Rudolph, Cupid, Vixen, Dasher, Comet, Blitzen, Donner, Dancer.

RACING REINDEER:
1st = B, 2nd = A, 3rd = C

38–39 FESTIVE PUZZLES

CANDY CANES:
There are 6 red candy canes and 5 green ones, so there are more red ones.

PRESENT SPOTTING:
1 = ◯ 2 = ◯ 3 = ◯

STARS SUDOKU:

CHRISTMASSY FIREPLACE:

SNOWSTORM SHAPE:
The shape is a star.

DING DONG!: String B

TREE TROUBLE: There are 15 trees.

42–43 RED AND GREEN

DRESS THE ELVES:
15 elves are wearing red.

ODDS AND EVENS:
There are more 'even' shapes.

TREE-ANGLES:

CANDIED CODES:
1 C STOCKING
2 B SNOWBALL
3 A SLEIGHBELLS

44–45 TOY SHOPPING

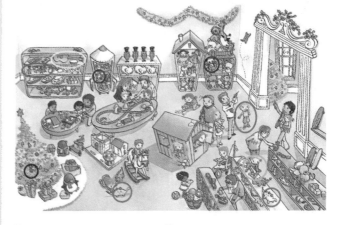

- ◯ panda
- ◯ someone holding a rabbit
- ◯ purple dinosaurs
- ◯ guitar
- ◯ spaceman
- ◯ reindeer decoration
- ◯ boy with blue shoes
- ◯ cowboys
- ◯ girl with a jigsaw puzzle

46-47 CHRISTMAS MYSTERIES

CRYPTIC INVITATION:

CHRISTMAS MOVIE MIX-UP:

FESTIVE LETTERS: No.

PRESENT RENDEZVOUS: MEET ME AT TEN IN THE TRAIN STATION BETH

CHRISTMAS BONE BRAIN-TEASER: Bone 17 is Noodle's bone.

48-49 AT THE MARKET

- ◯ bears
- ◯ train
- ◯ striped balls
- ◯ reindeer toy
- ◯ candy canes
- ◯ big chocolate heart
- ◯ robots
- ◯ marbles

TOY TIME:

WOODEN PUZZLE: C

CHRISTMAS FOOD:
OTH AHCEOLTCO = HOT CHOCOLATE
GSAASUSE = SAUSAGES
TSEUSCTHN = CHESTNUTS
EGNARDGIEBR = GINGERBREAD
ABDEK TOPOTA = BAKED POTATO

DECORATION SUDOKU:

52-53 STARRY NIGHT
STAR PATH:

54-55 STREET LIGHTS

LIGHT SHAPES:
The fifth shape is a triangle. From left to right, each shape has two fewer sides.

JUMBLE BELLS:
DECORATIONS, GARLANDS

STAR LIGHTS:

SYMMETRICAL CIRCLES:
These two lights are symmetrical:

BRIGHT BIRDS:
From left to right: red, green, orange, yellow, blue.

56-57 SANTA'S ELVES

SORTING LETTERS:
Olaf - RED, Erica - GREEN, Stefan - WHITE, Greta - NO STAMP, Henrik - SQUARE

TOYMAKERS:
B has made the most – 6. A made 4 and C made 5.

ELF AND SEEK: There are 12 elves.

IMPISH IMPOSTER:

58-59 SHOPPING DASH

CHRISTMAS CODE:
List: APPLES, TREE, SCARF, LIGHTS, BALL
No, he hasn't picked up the correct things.

TOY-SHOPPING SPRINT:

PRESENT PAIRS:
Yes, she has two of each thing.

RACE TO PAY:
Emily wins, with 29 points.

WHICH BAG?:
Bag number 9.

Additional design by Vickie Robinson, Melissa Gandhi and Holly Lamont

This edition first published in 2020 by Usborne Publishing Ltd., Usborne House, 83-85 Saffron Hill, London EC1N 8RT, England. usborne.com © 2020, 2019, 2012 Usborne Publishing Ltd. The name Usborne and the devices ♕♘ are Trade Marks of Usborne Publishing Ltd. All rights reserved. No part of this publication may be reproduced, stored in a retrieval system or transmitted in any form or by any means, electronic, mechanical, photocopying, recording or otherwise without the prior permission of the publisher. UE. This edition first published in America 2020. EDC, Tulsa, Oklahoma 74146 usbornebooksandmore.com